Demon Dribbler

Jonny Zucker

Illustrated by Jacopo Camagni

First published in 2014
by Franklin Watts

Text © Jonny Zucker 2014
Illustrations by Jacopo Camagni © Franklin Watts 2014
Cover design by Peter Scoulding

Franklin Watts
338 Euston Road
London NW1 3BH

Franklin Watts Australia
Level 17/207 Kent Street
Sydney, NSW 2000

A CIP catalogue record for this book
is available from the British Library.

(pb) ISBN: 978 1 4451 2616 6
(ebook) ISBN: 978 1 4451 2620 3
(Library ebook) ISBN: 978 1 4451 2624 1

1 3 5 7 9 10 8 6 4 2

Printed and bound by CPI Group (UK) Ltd, Croydon, CR0 4YY

Franklin Watts is a division of Hachette Children's Books,
an Hachette UK company.
www.hachette.co.uk

CONTENTS

CHAPTER 1
NEW KIT

"When are you going to get a decent kit to replace that rubbish one?" asked Gavin Mathers with a look of contempt.

It was football practice after school on Monday. The blue sky was dotted with patches of grey. A breeze rustled the trees that ringed the edges of the school field.

Leo Diamond was wearing his four-seasons-old City kit. The number ten on the back of the shirt had faded; several threads had come loose on the shorts.

"It doesn't matter what kit you wear," snapped Leo. "It's how you play!"

"Well, I haven't seen any Premier League players wearing awful kit," said

Gavin, hands on his hips. His City kit
was brand new. It looked like it had
only just come out of the shop.

"Shut it, Gavin," said Leo's best
mate, Mac.

"What's going on over there?"
demanded Mr Cross.

Mr Cross was running Leo's school team at the moment. He was an OK coach but wasn't anywhere near as good as Mr Lawson. Mr Lawson had a UEFA B coaching licence, but was spending all of his time with the school's older teams.

"It's nothing," replied Leo.

"Good," nodded Mr Cross. "I want all of you to take turns dribbling down the pitch as close to the touchline as possible. Gavin, you're first."

He chucked Gavin a ball. Gavin dropped it on the ground and began racing down the right side of the pitch, just managing to keep the ball in play.

"Not bad," shouted Mr Cross. "It's you next, Leo."

Leo placed the ball and started down

the line, determined to keep the ball in play while going faster than Gavin. But when he was halfway down he gave the ball too hard a nudge and it went over the touchline. He dragged it back onto the pitch and continued his run. He had nearly made it to the end of the pitch when the ball drifted over the line again. His dribbling skills had let him down.

Angry with himself he made the last few yards and then ran back up the pitch just as Mac was preparing to take his go.

"That was all right, Leo," nodded Mr Cross, "but there were a couple of stray touches. You let the ball rule you rather than the other way round."

Gavin Mathers grinned smugly at Leo. Leo felt his cheeks burning red.

* * * * * * * * * * * * * * * * * *

"Mum," said Leo as the two of them sat down for supper that night. "Is there any chance I could get a new City kit?"

Leo's mum ladled some pasta onto his plate and sighed.

"I'm really sorry, Leo, but things are a bit tight at the minute. I've got to buy a new kettle, and the electric bill is due."

"Sure," nodded Leo, trying his best not to look upset. Gavin Mathers's words had got to him.

"Maybe in a couple of months," smiled his mum.

Leo's mum worked as a nurse at the local hospital and after paying the rent, buying food and keeping the flat warm there was never much to go around. And it wasn't as if Leo's dad helped with the money situation. He'd walked out on Leo and his mum quite a while ago and he only sent the occasional card and a little bit of cash from time to time.

* * * * * * * * * * * * * * * * * *

Leo lay in bed that night going over the events of football practice in his head. If he'd been concentrating harder would he have kept the ball on the right side of the touchline for his whole run? Or was it just that he wasn't technically good enough, that he lacked some unknown but important dribbling quality? And would things be better if Mr Lawson, not Mr Cross, was coaching his team?

He fell asleep with these questions whirling around his brain.

CHAPTER 2
LIGHT FLASH

Leo found it hard to concentrate in school the next day. He got told off in maths for daydreaming and was pulled up in science for doodling football players on the back of his book.

"Come on, Leo," said Miss Baines, his science teacher. "You're a clever lad, but you spend too much time focusing on your football and not enough time on your school work. Don't forget that only one in a million players ever make it to professional standard. You need to keep up with your school work so that other career choices are open to you."

Miss Baines was all right. She supported Liverpool and came to watch Leo's year team when they played. And Leo knew what she said was true. But he couldn't stop thinking about his dribbling skills and how to make them better.

After school Leo met Mac by the lockers.

"Fancy going to the park to have a kickabout?" asked Leo.

"Of course!" grinned Mac.

At the park, they passed to each other from ever increasing distances. Then Mac went in goal and Leo took shots at him. Leo was fairly pleased with his strike rate; he scored one out of every two attempts against Mac, who was an excellent keeper and a quick mover.

"Let's do some dribbling now," said Leo.

They marked out a long strip of the pitch with their jackets and jumpers. "I'll defend," said Mac. "You have to try and get past me."

Leo started dribbling over the muddy grass, controlling the ball with his right foot. As he approached Mac he tried to swerve round him to the left, but Mac stuck out a leg and snatched the ball. On his second try he just managed to get round Mac but on his third he was tackled again.

In frustration, Leo picked up the ball and whacked it into the air. It flew away from the grass and landed on top of the old park hut. It didn't come down.

"Chill out, Leo," said Mac. "Being tackled isn't the end of the world. And I hope you're going up there to get it because I'm not!"

"But dribbling is what gets you round players," insisted Leo. "It's what makes a team move forward. If I keep on getting stopped I won't be able to help the team in any way."

"The game's not just about dribbling," said Mac. "What about passing and shooting?"

Leo sighed deeply.

Mac's phone beeped and he looked at a message. "I've got to go, Leo. Don't be too hard on yourself. You'll get there."

Mac gave Leo a friendly pat on the shoulder and then headed for the park's exit.

Leo kicked at a clod of mud and then walked over to the hut. It was easy to climb up onto the flat roof. The ball was lying in a shallow pool of water in the centre of the roof.

But as Leo walked across the roof he stopped. There was an old football collectors' card lying just by his foot. He bent down to pick it up. Suddenly

Leo felt a sizzling heat on his body and a flash of white light momentarily blinded him.

A couple of seconds later the light flash vanished, but he was no longer on the roof of the park hut.

He was on a beach.

CHAPTER 3
NUMBER 10

It was early evening and the sunlight was beginning to fade. In the distance people were drifting away from the sand to the bars and cafés that threw out strips of light. The waves lapped gently and the delicious smells of barbecued meat and vegetables drifted through the air. The only person close by was someone sitting in a deckchair with their back to him.

Leo walked over to the deckchair and cleared his throat. He'd have to ask this person where on earth he was and where the park had gone. There was a shuffling sound as the figure in the deckchair stood up and slowly turned round.

A bolt of energy hit Leo in the centre of his chest, because he found himself facing none other than Edson Arantes do Nascimento, otherwise known as... Pelé! He was wearing a yellow Brazil tracksuit and scuffed white trainers.

"I'm glad you could make it," nodded Pelé.

"Is this a dream?" asked Leo, rubbing his eyes and then opening them again.

"No," smiled Pelé. "Welcome to Copacabana Beach."

"What? I'm in Brazil?" gasped Leo.

Pelé nodded. "You're in Rio de Janeiro. Walk with me. I have a few things to tell you."

Leo fell into step with Pelé, the sand warm on the soles of his shoes as the great man shared some of his story. "I grew up very poor, Leo, so poor that I couldn't afford to buy a football. Do you know what I played with?"

Leo shook his head.

"A sock filled up with newspaper, tied by a string. And if that failed I used a grapefruit."

Leo was astounded.

"I played in the streets, I played in backyards. I had nothing but I was happy. The fact that we didn't have much money never bothered me. As long as I could play football, life was good."

"What about food?" asked Leo.

"We just about had enough to eat, but what I'm trying to tell you is it doesn't matter where you come from, or how little money your family has. Football is about determination to learn and the desire to pick up new skills. In these areas money is irrelevant."

"What about your natural ability?" asked Leo, digging his fingernails into his forearm to confirm he was actually here in Brazil talking to the most famous player of all time.

"Of course it helps if you have some natural ability, but lots of the world's finest players didn't stand out when they first started playing. It was through their dedication that they achieved greatness. Unfortunately, most people don't have that dedication. I have told young people for years and years that practice is everything."

They had reached a wooden shack and both leaned against its corrugated iron front.

"But if you couldn't afford a ball, how did you get to be so good?" asked Leo. "You didn't play for Santos or Brazil using a sock."

Pelé laughed. "The sock was pretty good, but from a young age I realised

I would have to make some money so I worked part time as a servant in the teashops of my home town. The pay wasn't great but it got me enough money to buy a proper football."

"I've got a proper ball and my mum and I have enough money to eat," said Leo, "but I want to become a demon dribbler, you know, someone who glides past people with the ball stuck to his feet. I need to prove my skills to the kids on my football team and to my coach."

"Well it's a good thing you're here then," grinned Pelé, reaching down by the side of the shack. He lifted up a white ball with the Brazil insignia on its front. "How about a little coaching?"

Leo was so excited he almost

couldn't move. "I'd be totally, completely up for it," he managed to say.

"Good," nodded Pelé, dropping the ball onto the sand. "Because this is where we start."

CHAPTER 4
THE KING OF DRIBBLING

"The key to fine dribbling is ball control and fooling the opposing player," said Pelé. "You must make them think you're going to do one thing while you do something completely different."

"You mean pretend you're going right when you actually go left?"

"That is one way," agreed Pelé. "And the best way of doing this is the shoulder dip. Dip your left shoulder and they'll think you're going left while you actually go right; dip your right shoulder and go left when they think you're going right. It's a simple technique but it works many times. Try it, Leo."

Pelé pointed to a wooden telephone

mast. "That's your defender," he explained, "you've got to fool him."

Leo spent the next twenty minutes running at the wooden pole, dipping one shoulder and swerving his body the other way while trying to keep the ball under control. At first he bashed into the pole a few times or lost control of the ball, but with Pelé shouting encouragement he started to get the hang of it.

"OK," said Pelé. "Now we will focus on the need to use both feet."

"But I'm right footed," pointed out Leo. "I never use my left."

"Get that notion out of your head immediately, young man," smiled Pelé. "It is time for a change. Welcome your left foot to the world of football. Let's get you running with the ball up to that red lifeguard station, using both feet."

Leo took a deep breath and started his run. He pushed the ball between his right and left foot. It felt weird but he was completely focused. The ball slipped away from his left foot a few times, but he kept going.

"And now back!" shouted Pelé.

Leo made the return journey, the ball drifting away a couple of times. Pelé made him do this two-footed, two-way journey another five times. Each time Leo got a tiny bit more used to using his left foot. He then did it five more times.

Leo was sweating by now, but his body felt electrified about the situation he was in. It was him and...Pelé!

"We've looked at the shoulder dip and using both feet," said Pelé. "Now comes the third and final factor."

Leo looked at the Brazilian expectantly. The chink of glasses sounded nearby and a bell rang somewhere in the distance.

"I want you to imagine the ball is part of your body."

Leo closed his eyes and pictured a ball connected to his right foot. He opened his eyes.

"If it's part of you, releasing it is like losing a bit of your body, and you can't do that. If someone tries to take it off you, you must protect it fiercely. Do you get me?"

Leo nodded.

"You will start with the ball, but I will do my best to snatch it away from you."

What followed was one of the most amazing moments of Leo's life. Out on the soft sands of Copacabana Beach he ran in lines, arcs and circles, keeping the ball as close to his feet as possible. And all the while, Pelé — the number 10 of all number 10s — pursued him, trying to reclaim the ball, sometimes successfully, sometimes unable to achieve this.

"OK, OK!" laughed Pelé. "STOP."

Reluctantly, Leo tapped the ball over to join his mentor.

"If you want to be a killer dribbler, the things I have shown you must be practised. Time and time again. Your feet will do the work, but your brain will control them. And don't just stick to what I've shown you. If you suddenly have an incredible idea and your team isn't at risk, then try the unusual. It might just work. And one other thing to remember Leo; someone saying your kit looks old is nothing to do with football. They are cruel but empty words."

Leo thought of his battered City kit and Gavin's taunting, and suddenly neither of those things seemed to matter to him.

"Listen, I have to go. Good luck with your practice," said Pelé.

"Thanks for everything," grinned Leo, "it's been amazing!" As he bent down to hand the ball back to Pelé, the wind whipped up the sand around him.

CHAPTER 5
A POINT TO PROVE

A second later, Leo was back on the roof of the park hut, staring down at the football card of Pelé. He picked his ball out of the puddle and chucked it back down onto the grass.

Climbing down he marvelled at what had just happened. Was it a dream? Had he imagined it, even though it felt so real? In a way it didn't matter. He'd just been shown the most vital skills in dribbling by the most legendary of dribblers. It was wild! It was mad! But it was also incredibly useful.

There were a few people walking dogs and some kids screaming with high-pitched delight in the little play park. But the football pitch was all Leo's. It was just after 4 pm. His mum wouldn't be home from work until 5.30-ish. There was plenty of time to practise what Pelé had taught him.

Shoulder dips, using two feet, keep the ball close.

Leo grabbed a few long branches lying next to a huge oak tree. He pressed them into the ground in a triangle shape. The branches would deputise for opposing players. He had to get past them and round them using his dribbling skills.

Leo ran, he dipped both shoulders, he switched between feet, pushing his left foot to do things it had never done before, and he worked on keeping the ball as close to his feet as possible.

Sure, he knocked the branches over several times, but he didn't let that get him down. Back into the earth they went and he resumed his dribbling.

He was so caught up in his training that he didn't track the passage of time. When he next looked at his watch it was 6 pm. He grabbed his ball and raced home.

* * * * * * * * * * * * * * * * * * *

A couple of days later, Leo and Mac were kicking a ball to each other by the back of the science block at school. Thoughts of Pelé and the dribbling coaching had been almost constantly in Leo's mind since his stint on Copacabana beach. These thoughts vanished, though, when Leo saw Gavin Mathers strolling over towards them and then sitting on a wall.

"Watching you two is like watching a couple of sparrows," laughed Gavin as Leo and Mac picked up on their passing again. "Absolutely puny and hopeless!"

"Get lost, Gavin!" snarled Leo.

Instead of backing off, Gavin jumped down from the wall, grabbed the ball and booted it as hard as he could. It arced through the air and cleared the fence separating the school from the houses backing onto it.

"Oops!" laughed Gavin.

Leo started to run at Gavin, but Mac held him back. "Don't let that idiot get to you," said Mac. "He doesn't deserve any attention."

Gavin cheered so loud it looked like he'd just won a million pounds.

Leo and Mac headed towards the fence to retrieve the ball.

Gavin Mathers really needs to be brought down a peg or two, seethed Leo.

CHAPTER 6
THE GREATEST

Leo was in a bad mood at the start of school the next day. The man in the garden where Gavin had kicked the ball hadn't been too happy. Leo had trampled on some of his prized rosebushes as he retrieved the ball.

But after school, Leo's thoughts turned back to Pelé. Instead of going home, he popped into his local library and into the sports section. Among the books about the modern Premier League, the history of football and some biographies of today's stars, were three books about Pelé. Leo took all three over to an empty table and sat down to look at them.

He knew that millions saw Pelé as the best player ever, and he was aware that the guy's stats would be pretty amazing. But what he discovered totally blew his mind. He pulled a piece of paper and a pen out of his school bag and started jotting down some of the main facts about the man:

He scored a total of 1,283 goals for club and country.

He was signed by Brazilian club, Santos, when he was 15.

At 17 he became the youngest-ever player to win the World Cup. That was in 1958 when Brazil beat Sweden 5–2 in the final.

He won three World Cups, two World Club Championships and nine Sau Paulo State Championships.

Pelé scored 92 hat-tricks, scored four on 31 occasions, five on 6 occasions, and once scored eight.

His first goal in the World Cup finals was against Wales in the 1958 quarter final, which Brazil won 1—0.

In 1967 a 48-hour ceasefire was declared in Nigeria so that opposing troops (the Federal troops and the Rebel troops who were fighting each other) could watch Pelé play on a visit to the war-torn nation.

Legendary Hungarian player Ferenc Puskás said: "The greatest player in history was Di Stefano. I refuse to classify Pelé as a player. He was above that."

Tarcisio Burgnich, the Italian defender who once marked Pelé, said: "I told myself before the game that he was made of skin and bone just like everyone else. But I was wrong."

With each piece of information Leo's admiration for the man grew. He was just looking at a black-and-white photo of Pelé in his early days at Santos, when his body suddenly heated up again and a blinding flash of light crashed into his face.

When he opened his eyes a few seconds later, he was no longer in the library with the books on Pelé. He was inside a gigantic football stadium. And a match was in full swing.

CHAPTER 7
WELCOME TO MEXICO

The crowd was almost deafening. There were roars and cheers and wild cries. It was like a huge party atmosphere, with a football game as its centrepiece.

Leo instantly recognised the Brazil team in their yellow shirts, blue shorts with a vertical stripe, and white socks. They had the ball and were passing it around very smoothly, maintaining possession and showing good control. But who were the other team in their turquoise tops, black shorts and black socks? He didn't need to wait long to find out because when there was a break in the play, the Brazilian number ten stepped from his outline and ran

over to Leo.

"Pelé!" gasped Leo. "What's going on?"

"This is the Estadio Jalisco in Guadalajara, Mexico," replied Pelé. "It's June 17th, 1970, and we're fifteen minutes into the second half of the 1970 World Cup semi-final."

"Unreal!" mouthed Leo.

"We're playing Uruguay," explained Pelé. "It's 1—1. Cubilla scored for them in the 18th minute. We were all shocked as we'd had more of the play."

"Who scored for you?"

"Clodoaldo got one back for us in injury time at the end of the first half."

Pelé then frowned.

"What is it?" asked Leo.

"Uruguay are playing a very dirty game," sighed Pelé. "Every time it looks like one of our players is going to break away, one of their lot takes out our legs. It's so frustrating. The referee booked three of their players — Mujica, Fontes and Maneiro — in the first half, but it doesn't seem to have made any difference."

"So you've been getting lots of free kicks?"

"Plenty," nodded Pelé, "but we prefer

open play. Uruguay's kind of violent game is against the spirit of football."

"But why am I here?" asked Leo, watching a series of huge Brazilian flags being waved in the stands.

"It's time to test out your dribbling skills," smiled Pelé. "It's exactly the kind of match where you can use everything I showed you on Copacabana beach. You need to fool these Uruguayans; use your speed and ball control. You can do it. I've seen your potential."

The referee blew his whistle for play to restart.

"But...but—" tried Leo.

"There's no time for hesitation," said Pelé. "You're on!"

CHAPTER 3
PENALTY!

Leo felt a massive surge of adrenaline shooting around his body as he ran onto the left side of the pitch and slipped into Pelé's outline. This was no match in the park; this was a World Cup semi-final! He had to do everything the Brazilian genius had shown him:

Shoulder dips, using two feet, keep the ball close.

He jogged around a bit to get warmed up and watched the action over on the right side. Within two minutes he was involved. He received the ball with his left foot on the left side of the pitch, just inside the Brazil half. A Uruguay defender tried to hold him back but he broke away.

This was his chance. He focused on all Pelé had told him and broke into a run, pushing the ball ahead of him three times with his right foot as he bore down on the penalty area. He touched it with his left foot as a swarm of Uruguay defenders raced to catch him, shouting out instructions at each other.

Leo was now just yards from the penalty area and the ball was in his control. If he could bypass the last couple of Uruguay defenders, his dribbling would lead him to a shooting position. He dipped his right shoulder to make it look like he was going to go right with his right foot, but then he flicked it past a defender with his left foot. He was now in the penalty area.

He was going to shoot.

But the Uruguay number two, Atilio Ancheta, had plans for Leo and he hacked him down with a vicious challenge.

"PENALTY!" shouted Leo, as he toppled to the ground. His team-mates ran towards him, waving their arms in the air at the referee and pointing at the penalty spot. The referee however, insisted that the foul had taken place outside the penalty area. He waved the Brazil players away. Leo stood up and shook his head. Ancheta didn't even get a yellow card.

A couple of Uruguay players offered Leo their hands to help him up but he refused them.

After the excitement of his run, the ball was placed on the ground a yard outside the area. His team-mates instructed him to take the free kick. He steeled himself and struck the ball. It went high over the goal. All of his good work had come to nothing.

"Keep your head up!" shouted Pelé from the touchline. "There's everything still to play for!"

From the resulting Uruguay goal kick, Leo watched the ball bounce and then struck it on the volley from forty yards out. It was a bold shot, but it went straight into the keeper's hands. Leo got shouts of encouragement from the other Brazil players, and this made him even more determined.

For the next ten minutes, the ball travelled to both penalty areas, but the Uruguay fouls kept coming. After one harsh challenge, Leo felt anger boiling inside him. There was about fifteen minutes left of the game and, if it went on like this, the Brazil players would be kicked into submission. Uruguay would nick a goal and that would be that. Leo ran down the pitch with a sinking feeling of dread in his chest.

CHAPTER 9
MAGNIFICENT MOVES

Then on 76 minutes everything changed. Jairzinho passed the ball to Leo, and with his back to the Uruguay goal, Leo flicked it backwards to Tostao who released Jairzinho on the right wing. Keeping the defender at bay, Jairzhino fired a low shot that evaded the Uruguay keeper and smashed into the net. It was 2–1!

The Brazil fans erupted, and Leo joined all of the Brazil players mobbing Jairzinho. He was incredibly proud of his contribution to the move. The flick had really sped things on their way. Leo's joy was tempered a few minutes later when Fontes — the Uruguay number fifteen — cut him down. Leo lay on the floor in pain as the Brazil physio raced onto the pitch and started massaging his leg. Luckily though, the pain eased off and Leo stood up. But he wasn't sure how much more of this savagery he could stand.

He received a whack in the jaw several minutes later but carried on, knowing that a place in the World Cup final beckoned. Brazil had to keep the Uruguay side out. As the clock hit

90 minutes Leo felt the excitement
in the stadium rise to a new level. He
was just past the centre circle in the
Uruguay half, when a Uruguay defender
headed the ball to his feet.

OK, thought Leo, I'll show them skill
beats violence.

Shoulder dips, using two feet, keep
the ball close.

He controlled the ball and pushed it
forward with his left foot. Striding up
the pitch he switched to his right foot.
He was now at the edge of the penalty
area and dipped his left shoulder,
making as if to shoot with his right
foot. But then he twisted, touched the
ball with his left, then his right and
then his left, before finally using his
right foot to pass into the centre.

Rivelino was there, waiting for the ball, and he thumped it hard into the back of the Uruguay net.

3—1, and Leo had provided the assist!

The Brazil fans went wild! There was no way Uruguay could stop them. The 1970 World Cup final beckoned. Leo glanced to the touchline and saw Pelé

— the real Pelé — leaping up and down, invisible to everyone but Leo.

Uruguay kicked off, but Brazil soon had the ball again. Number nine, Tostao, was on the left, just inside the opposition half. Leo looked at Tostao and instantly knew what he was going to do.

So Leo sprinted as Tostao hit a pass between the last two Uruguay defenders.

What had Pelé said?

If the team isn't in danger, go for something unusual. Well, Brazil were certainly not in danger and a crazy thought entered Leo's brain. He ran towards the Uruguay keeper, Mazurkiewicz, and made it look like he was going right to take a shot. But instead he ran left past the keeper without touching the ball. The keeper

was totally fooled and the ball shot
straight past him on the right. Leo then
collected the ball and quickly shot,
hoping to make it 4—1.

But in spite of his genius move, the
ball trailed just wide of the far post.
Leo was devastated at missing the goal,
but he knew he had just pulled off a
legendary move.

It was then that he heard Pelé calling. Leo ran over to the touchline.

"That dummy was incredible!" laughed Pelé. "And your dribbling has been fantastic. I couldn't have done better myself."

Praise from the Brazil number ten was pretty spectacular and for a few seconds Leo smiled to himself. But then Pelé motioned for them to swap places. So Leo stepped from the outline and Pelé stepped back in. Pelé patted Leo's back before he ran back onto the pitch.

The referee blew his whistle for full time and all of the Brazil coaching staff, physios and substitutes sprinted onto the pitch. They had won! As Leo watched, his body became very hot, and with a burst of white light, he vanished.

CHAPTER 10
SKILLING UP

Leo slowly opened his eyes. The majestic stadium was gone and he was back in the library with the three books about Pelé open. He shook his head and stared at a photo of the Brazilian number ten dipping his left shoulder, about to go right, while a dazed defender looked helplessly on.

* * * * * * * * * * * * * * * * * *

"I've been thinking," said Leo's mum as they sat talking in the kitchen that night. "I don't think it's fair that all of the other boys have bright new football kits and you have that tatty old one.

I've put a little bit of money aside for a rainy day and I've decided that I want to spend it on a kit."

The words of Pelé rippled through Leo's mind.

Someone saying your kit looks old is nothing to do with football. They are cruel but empty words.

"I don't need a new City kit," replied Leo. "When I get a Saturday job next year I'll buy it with the money I earn."

Leo's mum raised an eyebrow. "Are you sure?" she asked. "You're not just saying that."

"I'm totally sure," smiled Leo. "Having a new kit won't help me become a better player. It's really no big deal."

* * * * * * * * * * * * * * * * * *

The next day, in after-school football practice, Leo's head was still completely full of the Brazil vs Uruguay game and his role in it. Whether the whole thing had been a daydream or some kind of illusion didn't matter. What mattered was that he felt ten times more confident with his dribbling skills.

It was halfway through the practice. Mr Cross said they were now going to play a couple of five-a-side games. Before those kicked off, Mr Cross talked to the boys about zonal marking and the link between the defenders and the midfield/attackers. But as he wasn't the world's best coach, he went on for too long and he didn't sound as if he totally understood what he was saying. When he finally stopped talking and chose the sides, Leo and Mac were on the same team. Gavin Mathers was on the team facing them.

"I see you're still wearing that old tatty piece of cloth," smirked Gavin as the game kicked off. Leo said nothing. His response would be on the pitch.

After seven minutes with the score still 0—0, Leo picked up the ball just inside the opposition's half. One of their players, a kid called Paul, went to tackle Leo, but Leo pushed the ball through his legs and raced forward. Another player called Carl dived in, but Leo lifted the ball over Carl's outstretched body.

He had sight of goal, but then Gavin raced towards him, blocking his way.

Shoulder dips, using two feet, keep the ball close.

Leo dropped his left shoulder and touched the ball with his right foot. Gavin was instantly fooled and lunged in to get the ball. But in a lightning quick move, Leo flicked the ball rightwards with his left foot, leaving Gavin stranded on the ground.

With only the keeper to be beat, Leo dummied a pass to Mac and then smacked the ball with his right instep. It flew forwards and careered into the top left-hand corner of the goal.

"That dribbling was amazing!" shouted Mac, running over and high-fiving with Leo.

"Where do you think you are?" scowled Gavin, picking himself off the ground, his shiny new City kit streaked with dirt. "This isn't Brazil!"

Leo picked the ball out of the back of the net and hoofed it back to the centre circle for the restart. He grinned to himself. It was amazing how much you could learn...if you had the right coach and the right attitude.

FOOTBALL STAR POWER

There are four books to collect!

978 1 4451 2615 9 pb   978 1 4451 2619 7 ebook

Free-kick Pro
Jonny Zucker

978 1 4451 2616 6 pb   978 1 4451 2620 3 ebook

Demon Dribbler
Jonny Zucker

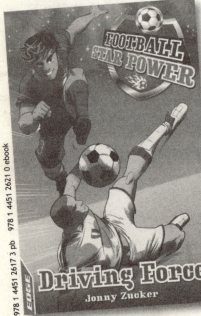

978 1 4451 2617 3 pb   978 1 4451 2621 0 ebook

Driving Force
Jonny Zucker

978 1 4451 2618 0 pb   978 1 4451 2622 7 ebook

Hottest Shot
Jonny Zucker